EASIEST KEYBOARD COLLECTION

Coldplay

WISE PUBLICATIONS
part of The Music Sales Group
London/New York/Paris/Sydney/Copenhagen/Berlin/Madrid/Tokyo

Published by
Wise Publications

Exclusive Distributors:
Music Sales Limited
14-15 Berners Street,
London W1T 3LJ, UK.
Music Sales Pty Limited
120 Rothschild Avenue,
Rosebery, NSW 2018,
Australia.

Order No. AM988889
ISBN 10: 1-84609-873-4
ISBN 13: 978-1-84609-873-4
This book © Copyright 2007 by Wise Publications.

Compiled by Nick Crispin.
Edited by Heather Slater.
Music arranged by Vasco Hexel.
Music processed by Paul Ewers Music Design.

Cover photograph © Steven Dewall / Retna

Printed in the EU.

Your Guarantee of Quality
As publishers, we strive to produce every book to the highest
commercial standards.
The music has been freshly engraved and the book has been carefully
designed to minimise awkward page turns and to make playing from
it a real pleasure.
Particular care has been given to specifying acid-free, neutral-sized
paper made from pulps which have not been elemental chlorine
bleached. This pulp is from farmed sustainable forests and was
produced with special regard for the environment.
Throughout, the printing and binding have been planned to ensure
a sturdy, attractive publication which should give years of enjoyment.
If your copy fails to meet our high standards, please inform us and
we will gladly replace it.

www.musicsales.com

Contents

CLOCKS

Words & Music by Guy Berryman, Chris Martin, Jon Buckland & Will Champion

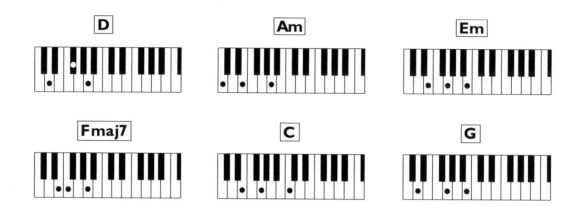

Voice: **Piano**

Rhythm: **16-Beat Pop**

Tempo: ♩ = 130

Lights go out and I can't be saved, tides that I tried to swim a-gainst, brought me down up-on my knees, oh, I beg, I beg and plead. Sing-ing; come out with things un-said, shoot an ap-ple off my head, and a trou-ble that can't be named, a ti-ger's wait-ing to be tamed. Sing-ing,

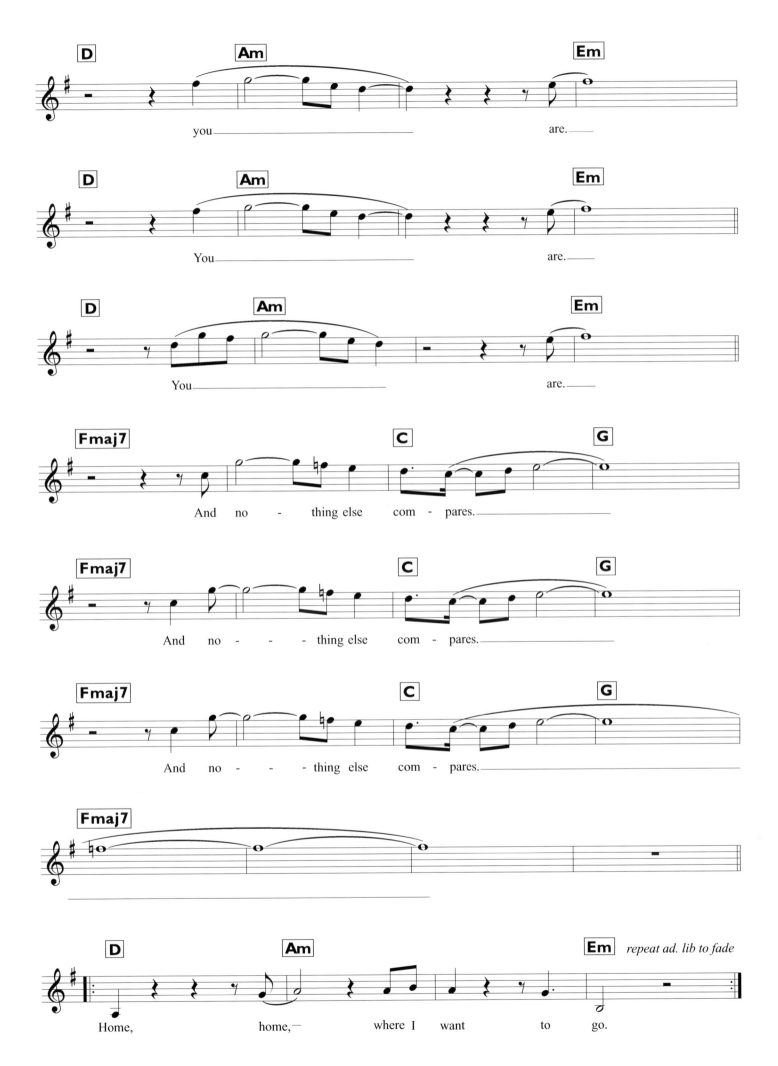

DON'T PANIC

Words & Music by Guy Berryman, Jon Buckland, Will Champion & Chris Martin

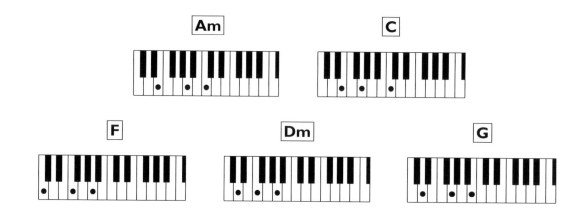

Voice: **Acoustic Guitar**

Rhythm: **Funk Rock**

Tempo: ♩ = 125

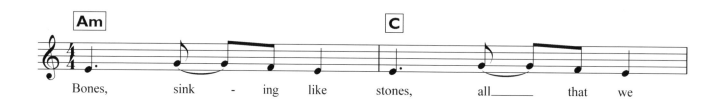

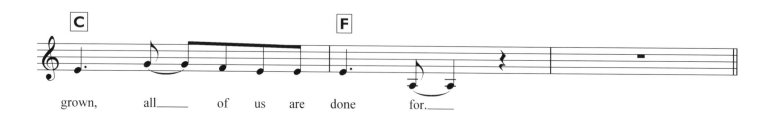

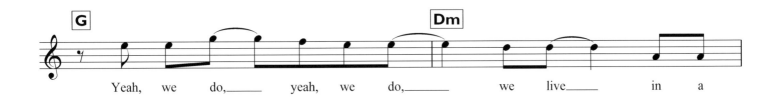

Yeah, we do,_____ yeah, we do,_____ we live_____ in a

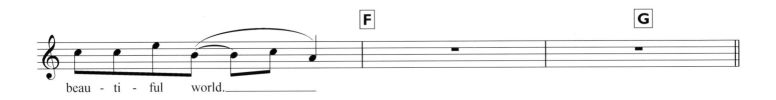

beau - ti - ful world._____

Bones, sink - ing like stones, all_____ that we fought for,_____

homes, pla - ces we've grown, all_____ of us are

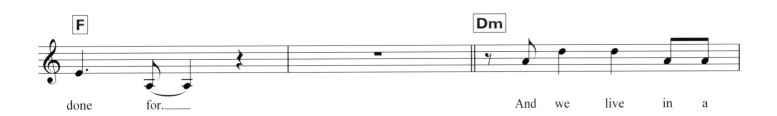

done for._____ And we live in a

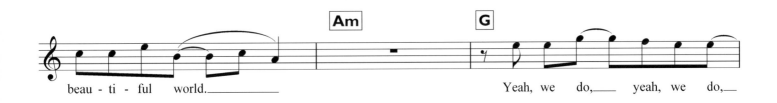

beau - ti - ful world._____ Yeah, we do,_____ yeah, we do,_____

_____ we live_____ in a beau - ti - ful world._____

EVERYTHING'S NOT LOST

Words & Music by Guy Berryman, Jon Buckland, Will Champion & Chris Martin

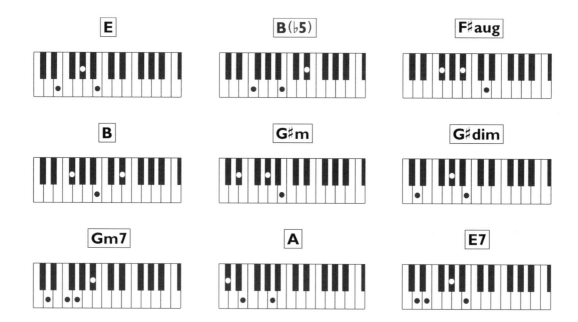

Voice: **Piano**

Rhythm: **Shuffle Rock**

Tempo: ♩ = 75

When you thought that it was ov - er_____

you could feel it all a - round._____ And ev-'ry-bo-dy's out to

get you._____ Don't you let it drag_ you down._____

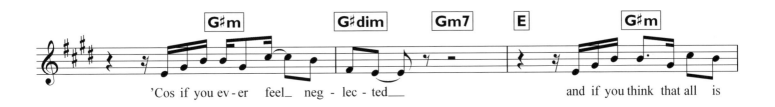

'Cos if you ev - er feel_ neg - lec - ted_ and if you think that all is

lost,_ I'll be count - ing up my de - mons yeah,_

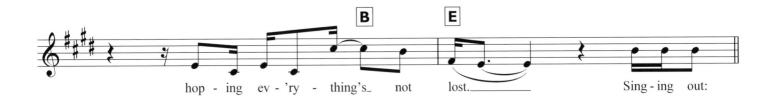

hop - ing ev - 'ry - thing's_ not lost._ Sing - ing out:

Oh, oh, oh, yeah,_ oh, oh, yeah,_

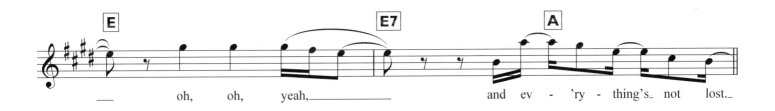

_ oh, oh, yeah,_ and ev - 'ry - thing's_ not lost._

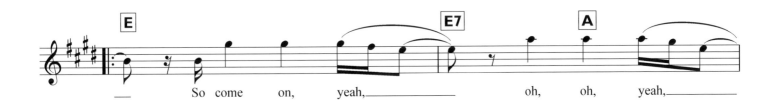

_ So come on, yeah,_ oh, oh, yeah,_

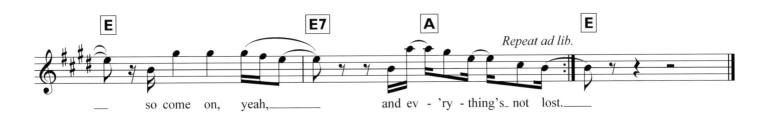

_ so come on, yeah,_ and ev - 'ry - thing's_ not lost._

FIX YOU

Words & Music by Coldplay, Guy Berryman, Chris Martin, Jon Buckland & Will Champion
© Copyright 2005 BMG Music Publishing Limited.
All Rights Reserved. International Copyright Secured.

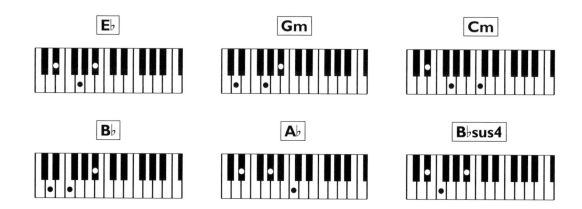

Voice: **Rock Organ**

Rhythm: **Soft Rock 2**

Tempo: ♩ = 70

When you   try your best but you don't suc - ceed.___   When you

get what you want   but   not what you   need.___   When you

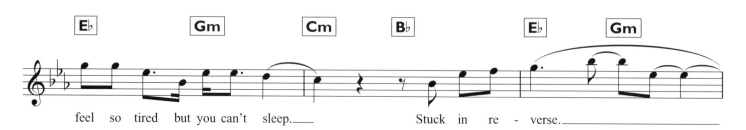

feel   so tired but you can't   sleep.___   Stuck   in   re - verse.___

—   And the tears___   come stream-ing down your face___   when you

GOD PUT A SMILE UPON YOUR FACE

Words & Music by Guy Berryman, Chris Martin, Jon Buckland & Will Champion

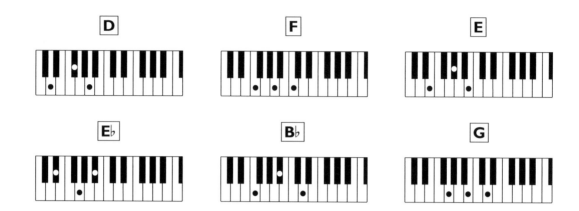

Voice: **Electric Guitar**

Rhythm: **Hard Rock**

Tempo: ♩ = 128

Where do we go? No-bo-dy knows.___

I've got-ta say I'm on my way___ down.

God give me style and give me grace.___

God put a smile up-on my face.___

THE HARDEST PART

Words & Music by Guy Berryman, Chris Martin, Jon Buckland & Will Champion

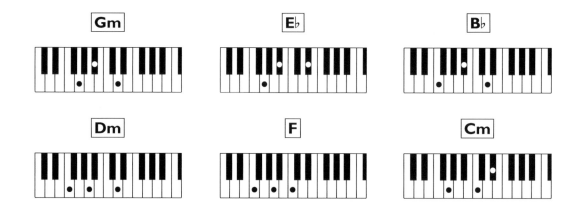

Voice: **Rock Organ**

Rhythm: **Rock 2**

Tempo: ♩ = **125**

And the hard - est part___ was let - ting go.___ Not

tak - ing part___ was the hard - est part.___

___ And the strang-

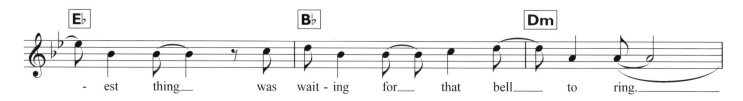

- est thing___ was wait - ing for___ that bell___ to ring.___

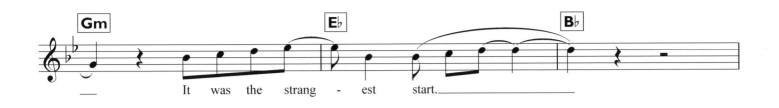

It was the strang - est start._____

I could feel____ it____ go down,____

bit - ter - sweet,____

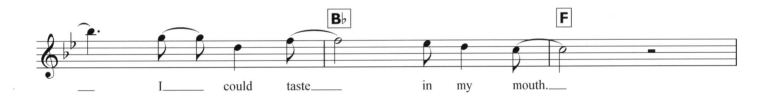

____ I____ could taste____ in my mouth.____

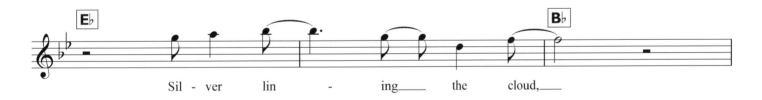

Sil - ver lin - ing____ the cloud,____

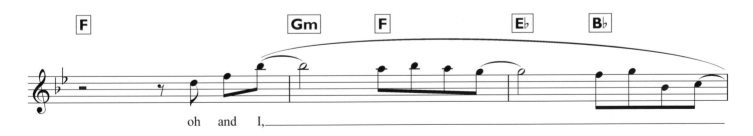

oh and I,_____

____ I wish that I could work it out.____

IN MY PLACE

Words & Music by Guy Berryman, Chris Martin, Jon Buckland & Will Champion

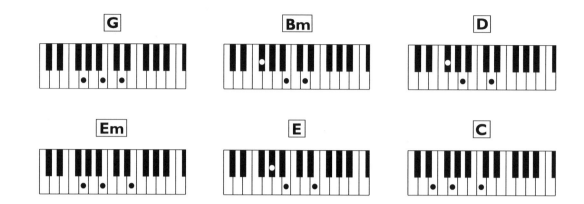

Voice: **Clarinet**

Rhythm: **Pop Rock I**

Tempo: ♩ = 72

In my place, in my_____ place were lines that I_____ could-n't

change. I was lost, oh yeah. And I was lost, I was

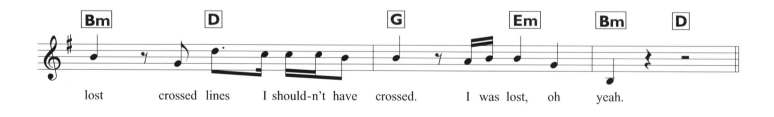

lost crossed lines I should-n't have crossed. I was lost, oh yeah.

Yeah,_____ how long must_ you wait for_____ it? Yeah,_ how

A MESSAGE

Words & Music by Guy Berryman, Chris Martin, Jon Buckland & Will Champion

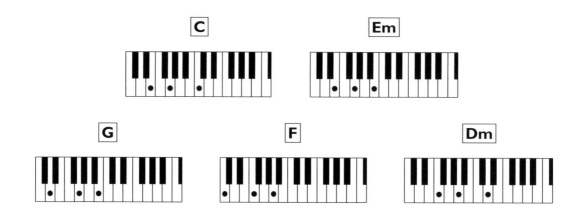

Voice: **New Age Pad**

Rhythm: **Straight Rock**

Tempo: ♩ = 120

POLITIK

Words & Music by Guy Berryman, Chris Martin & Will Champion

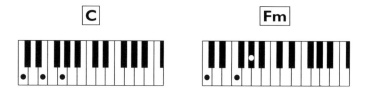

Voice: **Piano**

Rhythm: **Hard Rock**

Tempo: ♩ = 84

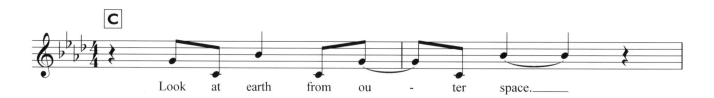

Look at earth from ou - ter space.____

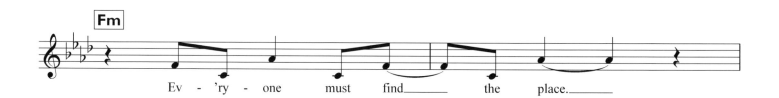

Ev - 'ry - one must find____ the place.____

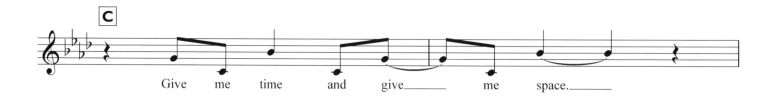

Give me time and give____ me space.____

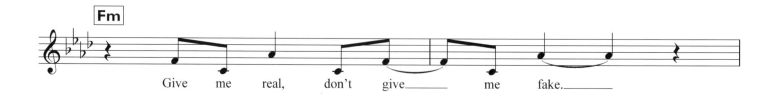

Give me real, don't give____ me fake.____

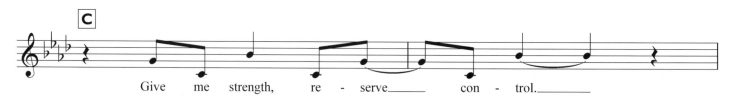

Give me strength, re - serve____ con - trol.____

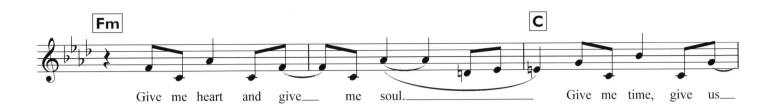

Give me heart and give me soul. Give me time, give us

a kiss and tell me your own Po - li - tik.

And o - pen up your

eyes. O - pen up your

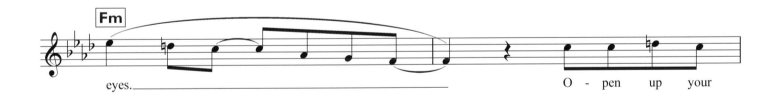

eyes. O - pen up your

eyes. O - pen up your eyes.

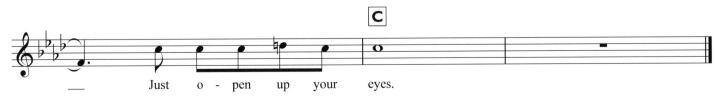

Just o - pen up your eyes.

A RUSH OF BLOOD TO THE HEAD

Words & Music by Guy Berryman, Chris Martin, Jon Buckland & Will Champion

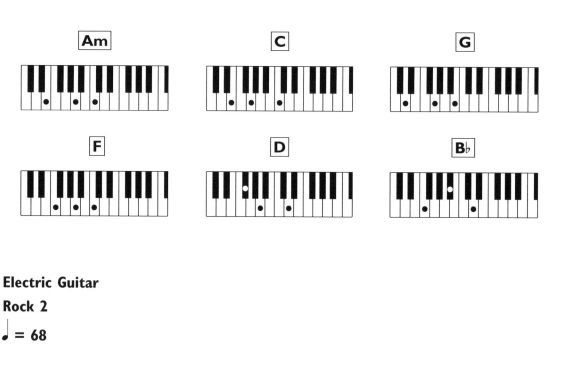

Voice: **Electric Guitar**

Rhythm: **Rock 2**

Tempo: ♩ = 68

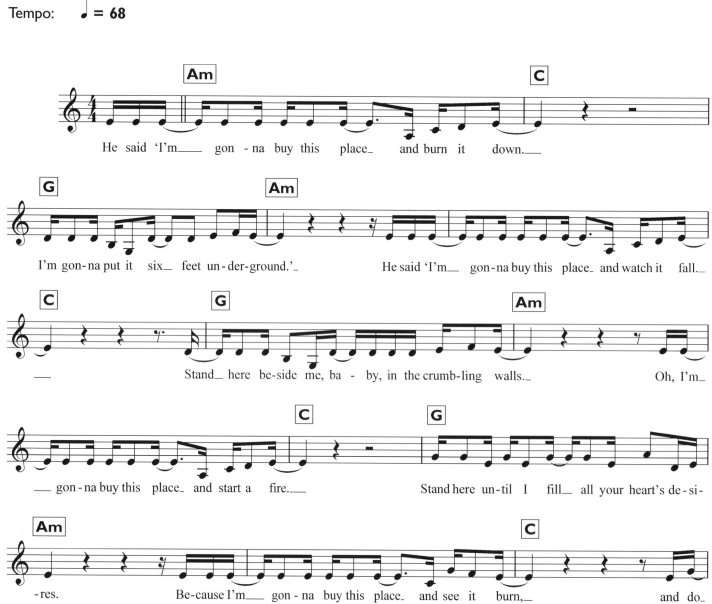

THE SCIENTIST

Words & Music by Guy Berryman, Chris Martin, Jon Buckland & Will Champion

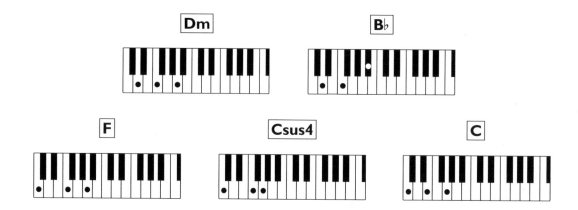

Voice: **Piano**

Rhythm: **Rock 1**

Tempo: ♩ = 74

Come up to meet___ you,___ tell you I'm sor - ry,___ you don't know how love-

- ly you are.___ I had to find___ you,___ tell you I need___

___ you___ and tell you I set___ you a - part.___ Tell me your sec-

- rets,___ and ask me your ques - tions.___ Oh, let's go back to___ the start.___

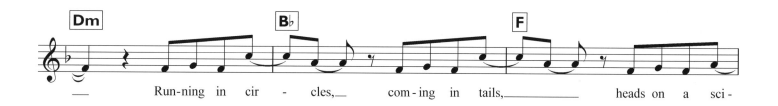

Run-ning in cir - cles,___ com-ing in tails,___ heads on a sci-

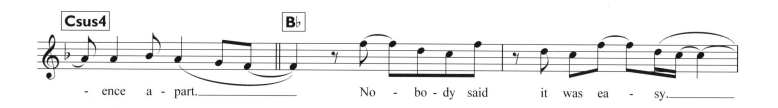

- ence a - part.___ No - bo-dy said it was ea - sy.___

___ It's___ such a shame___ for us to part.___ No - bo-dy said

it was ea - sy.___ No - one e - ver said it would be this___ hard.__

___ Oh, take me back to the start.___

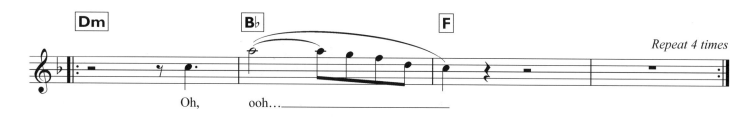

Oh, ooh…___

Repeat 4 times

SHIVER

Words & Music by Guy Berryman, Jon Buckland, Will Champion & Chris Martin

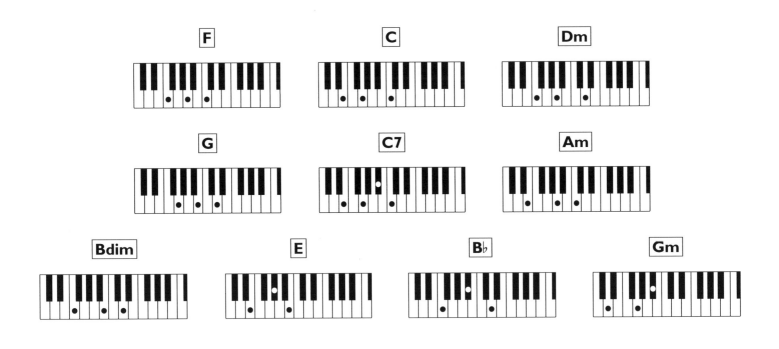

Voice: **Flute**

Rhythm: **Rock Ballad (12/8)**

Tempo: ♩. = 78

So I look in your di-rec-tion, but you pay me no at-ten-tion,_ do you?

I know you don't lis-ten to me 'cause you

say you see straight through me, don't you? And on and on___

___ from the mo-ment I wake,_ to the mo-ment I sleep,_ I'll be there by your side.

SPEED OF SOUND

Words & Music by Guy Berryman, Chris Martin, Jon Buckland & Will Champion

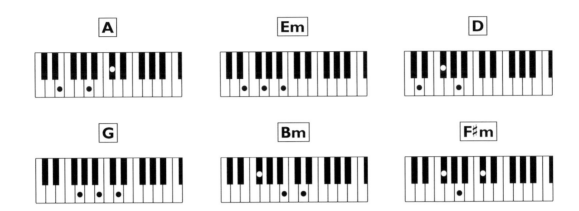

Voice: **New Age Pad**

Rhythm: **Hard Rock**

Tempo: ♩ = 122

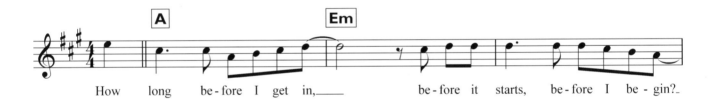

How long be-fore I get in,___ be-fore it starts, be-fore I be - gin?_

___ How long be-fore you de - cide,___ or be-fore I know_

___ what it feels___ like?___ Where to? Where do I go?_

___ If you ne - ver try,___ then you'll ne - ver know.___ How

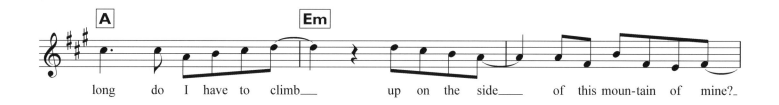

long do I have to climb___ up on the side___ of this moun-tain of mine?_

___ All that noise,___ and all that sound,_

___ all those pla -

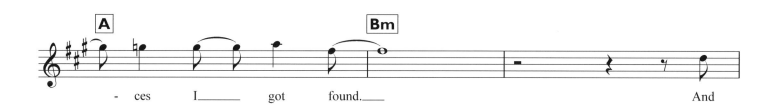

- ces I___ got found.___ And

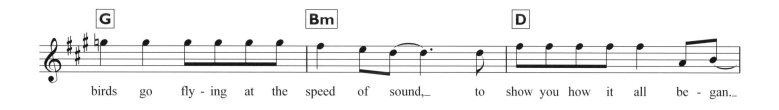

birds go fly - ing at the speed of sound,_ to show you how it all be - gan._

___ Birds___ came fly - ing from the un - der - ground,_ if you could

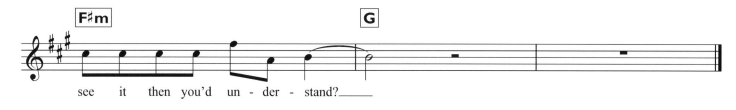

see it then you'd un - der - stand?_____

SPIES

Words & Music by Guy Berryman, Jon Buckland, Will Champion & Chris Martin

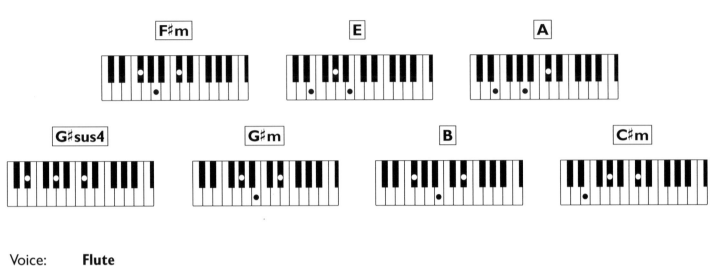

Voice: **Flute**

Rhythm: **Funk Rock**

Tempo: ♩ = 75

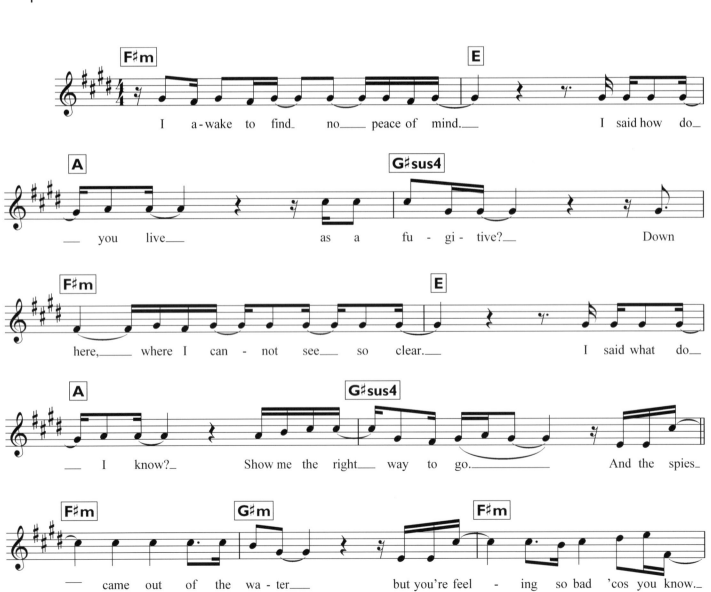

I a-wake to find no peace of mind. I said how do you live as a fu - gi - tive? Down here, where I can - not see so clear. I said what do I know? Show me the right way to go. And the spies came out of the wa - ter but you're feel - ing so bad 'cos you know.

SQUARE ONE

Words & Music by Guy Berryman, Chris Martin, Jon Buckland & Will Champion

TALK

Words & Music by Guy Berryman, Jon Buckland, Will Champion, Chris Martin, Ralf Hütter, Karl Bartos & Emil Schult

Voice: **Electric Guitar**

Rhythm: **16-Beat Rock**

Tempo: ♩ = **120**

TROUBLE

Words & Music by Guy Berryman, Jon Buckland, Will Champion & Chris Martin
© Copyright 2000 BMG Music Publishing Limited.
All Rights Reserved. International Copyright Secured.

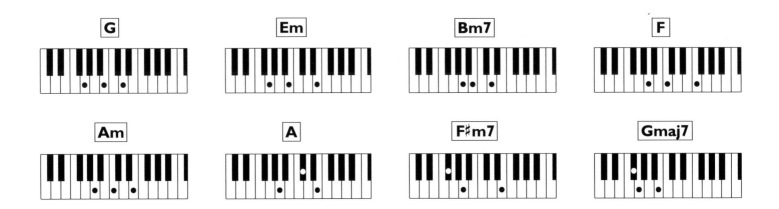

Voice: **Electric Piano 1**

Rhythm: **8-Beat Pop**

Tempo: ♩ **= 70**

Oh no, I see a spi-der web is tang-led up with

me and I lost my head, and thought of all the stu-pid things I'd

said.

Oh no, what's this? A spi-der web __ and I'm caught in the mid-dle,

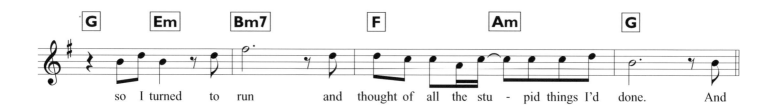

so I turned to run and thought of all the stu - pid things I'd done. And

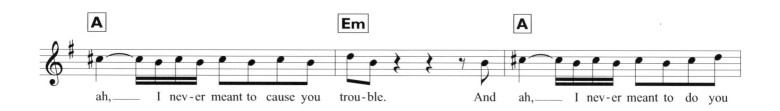

ah,____ I nev-er meant to cause you trou-ble. And ah,____ I nev-er meant to do you

wrong. And ah,____ well if I ev-er caused you trou-ble, and

oh no, I nev-er meant to do you harm. They spun a

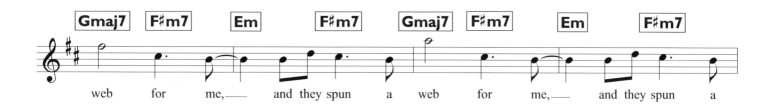

web for me,____ and they spun a web for me,____ and they spun a

web for me.____

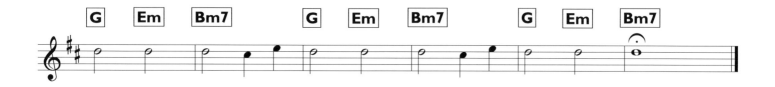

WARNING SIGN

Words & Music by Guy Berryman, Jon Buckland, Will Champion & Chris Martin

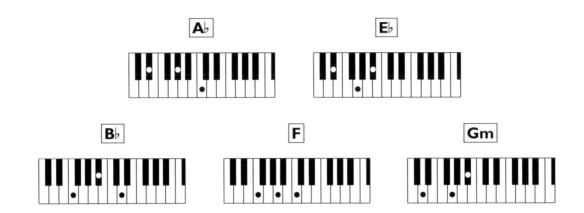

Voice: **Acoustic Guitar**

Rhythm: **Slow Rock**

Tempo: ♩ = 72

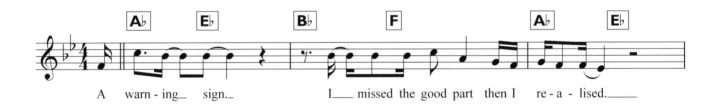

A warn-ing_ sign._ I_ missed the good part then I re-a-lised._

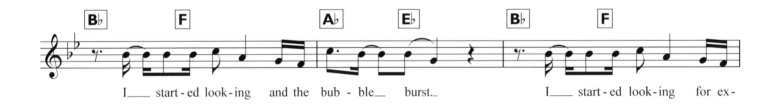

I_ start-ed look-ing and the bub-ble_ burst._ I_ start-ed look-ing for ex-

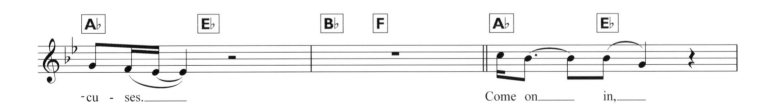

-cu - ses._ Come on_ in,_

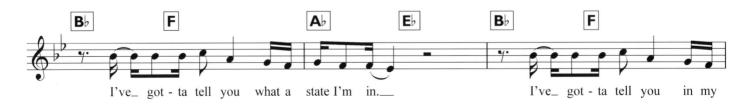

I've_ got-ta tell you what a state I'm in._ I've_ got-ta tell you in my

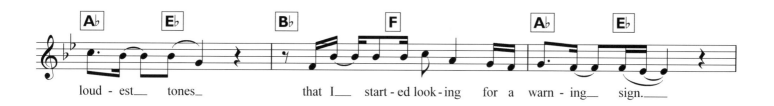

loud - est__ tones__ that I__ start - ed look - ing for a warn - ing__ sign.__

When the truth is:

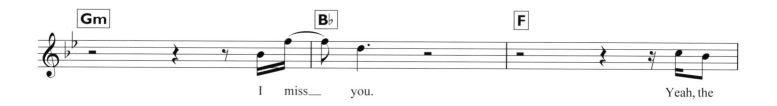

I miss__ you. Yeah, the

truth is that I miss__ you__ so.__

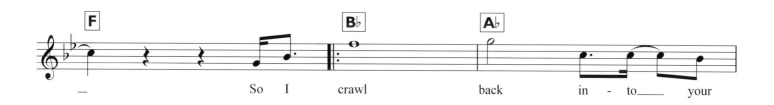

So I crawl back in - to__ your

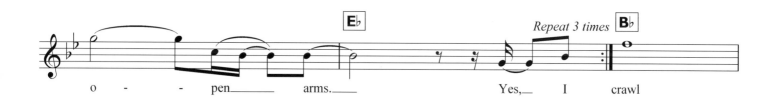

o - - pen__ arms.__ Yes,__ I crawl

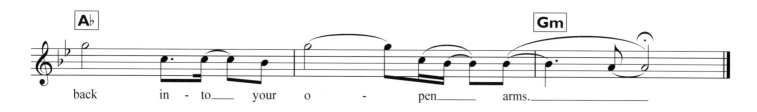

back in - to__ your o - pen__ arms.__

WHAT IF

Words & Music by Guy Berryman, Chris Martin, Jon Buckland & Will Champion
© Copyright 2005 BMG Music Publishing Limited.
All Rights Reserved. International Copyright Secured.

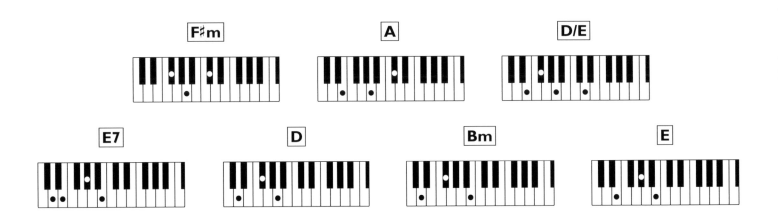

Voice: **Electric Piano**

Rhythm: **Rock 1**

Tempo: ♩ = **70**

What if there was_ no line,_____ No-thing wrong, no-thing

right?_____ What if there was_ no time_____ and no rea - son or

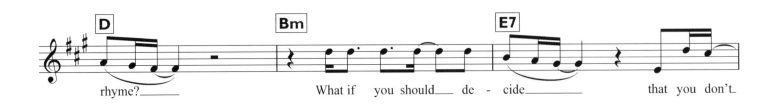

rhyme?_____ What if you should_ de - cide_____ that you don't

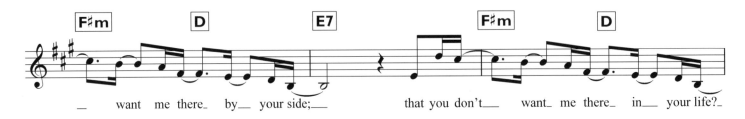

_ want me there_ by_ your side;_____ that you don't_ want_ me there_ in_ your life?_____

WHITE SHADOWS

Words & Music by Guy Berryman, Chris Martin, Jon Buckland & Will Champion

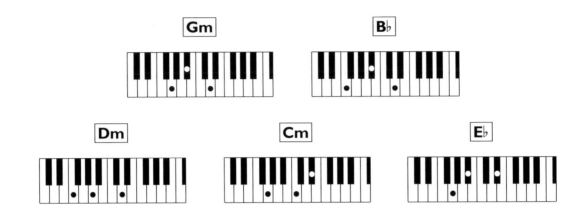

Voice: **Rock Organ**

Rhythm: **16-Beat Rock**

Tempo: ♩ = 125

X&Y

Words & Music by Guy Berryman, Chris Martin, Jon Buckland & Will Champion
© Copyright 2005 BMG Music Publishing Limited.
All Rights Reserved. International Copyright Secured.

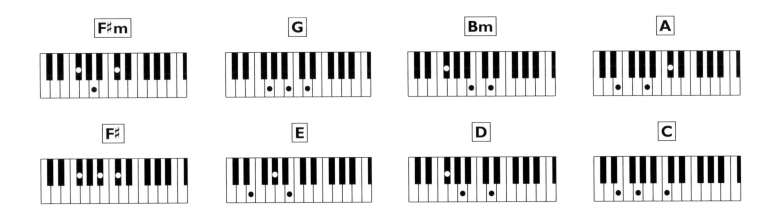

Voice: **Strings 1**

Rhythm: **Pop Rock**

Tempo: ♩ = 75

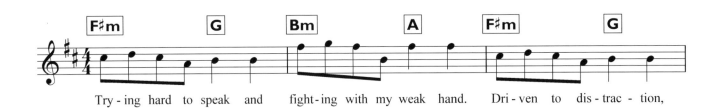

Try - ing hard to speak and fight-ing with my weak hand. Dri - ven to dis - trac - tion,

so part of the plan. When some-thing is bro - ken and you try to fix it,

try - ing to re - pair it a - ny way you can.

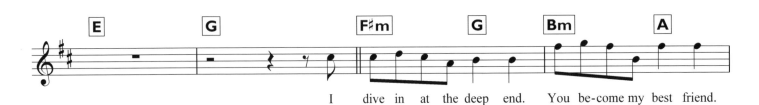

I dive in at the deep end. You be-come my best friend.

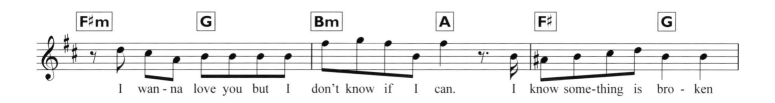

I wan-na love you but I don't know if I can. I know some-thing is bro-ken

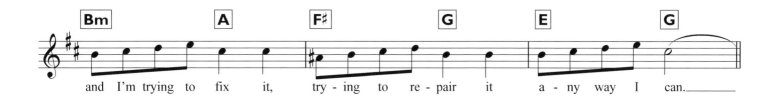

and I'm trying to fix it, try-ing to re-pair it a-ny way I can.___

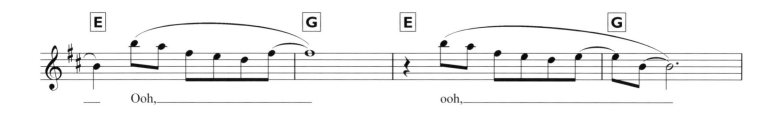

___ Ooh,___ ooh,___

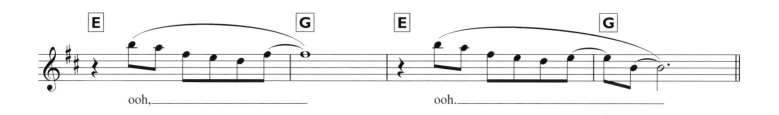

ooh,___ ooh.___

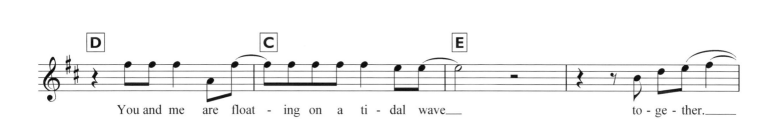

You and me are float-ing on a ti-dal wave___ to-ge-ther.___

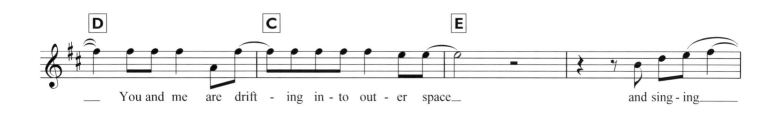

___ You and me are drift-ing in-to out-er space___ and sing-ing___

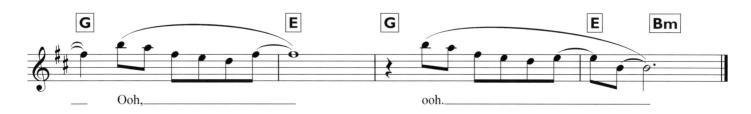

___ Ooh,___ ooh.___

YELLOW

Words & Music by Guy Berryman, Jon Buckland, Will Champion & Chris Martin

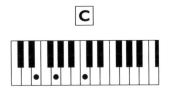 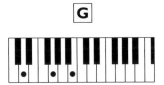 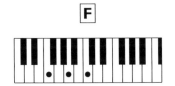 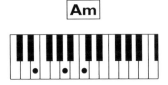

Voice: **Flute**

Rhythm: **Rock 1**

Tempo: ♩ = 84

Look at the stars, look how they shine for_____

___ you_____ and ev - 'ry - thing you do.___

___ Yeah, they were all_____ yel - low.___

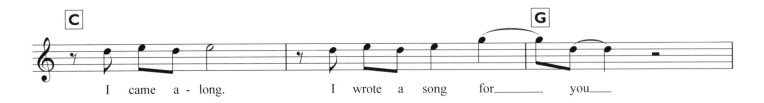

I came a - long. I wrote a song for_____ you___

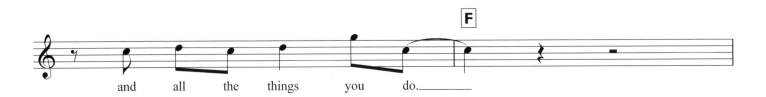

and all the things you do._____

And it was called_____ 'Yel - low'___

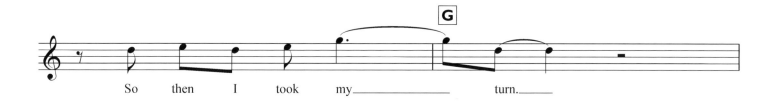

So then I took my_____ turn._____

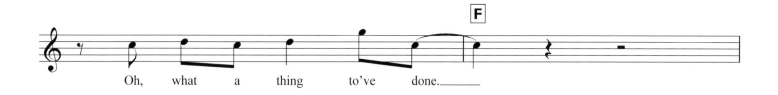

Oh, what a thing to've done._____

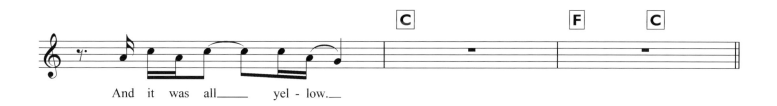

And it was all____ yel - low.__

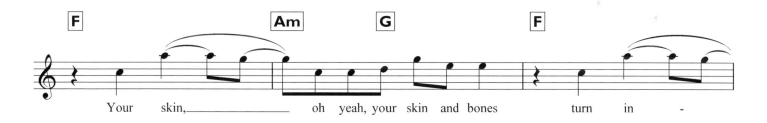

Your skin,_____ oh yeah, your skin and bones turn in -

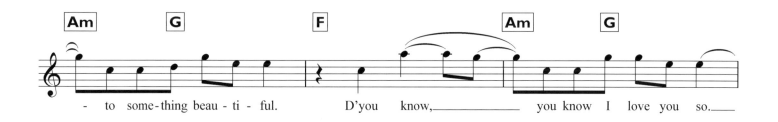

- to some-thing beau - ti - ful. D'you know,_____ you know I love you so.__

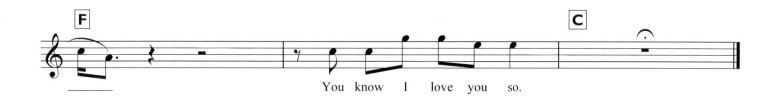

_____ You know I love you so.

EASIEST KEYBOARD COLLECTION

Easy-to-play melody line arrangements for all keyboards with chord symbols and lyrics. Suggested registration, rhythm and tempo are included for each song together with keyboard diagrams showing left-hand chord voicings used.

   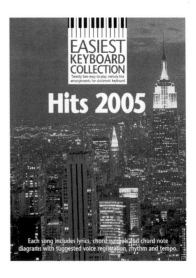

Karaoke Classics

The Best (Tina Turner),

Crazy (Patsy Cline),

Girls Just Want To Have Fun (Cyndi Lauper),

Hero (Enrique Iglesias),

Like A Prayer (Madonna),

(I've Had) The Time Of My Life (Bill Medley & Jennifer Warnes),

Like A Prayer (Madonna)

and 15 more big karaoke hits.

Order No. AM985072

Classics

Barcarolle (Offenbach),

Caprice No.21 (Paganini),

and 20 more classic themes, including New World Symphony (Dvořák),

Ode To Joy from Symphony No.9 (Beethoven),

Spring from *The Four Seasons* (Vivaldi), and

Swan Lake (Tchaikovsky).

Order No. AM952094

Christmas Hits

Over 20 favourite festive hits, including All I Want For Christmas Is You (Mariah Carey),

Blue Christmas (Elvis Presley),

I Saw Mommy Kissing Santa Claus (The Ronettes),

Lonely This Christmas (Mud),

and Walking In The Air – Theme from *The Snowman* (Aled Jones).

Order No. AM986964

Hits 2005

A great collection of 22 chart hits of 2005, including

Filthy/Gorgeous (Scissor Sisters),

Radio (Robbie Williams),

Room On The Third Floor (McFly),

Shiver (Natalie Imbruglia),

This Is The Last Time (Keane),

What You Waiting For (Gwen Stefani),

and Wisemen (James Blunt).

Order No. AM91982

Over 50 titles available in this series

Abba, Order No. AM959860

Ballads, Order No. AM952116

The Beatles, Order No. NO90686

Broadway, Order No. AM952127

Chart Hits, Order No. AM952083

Classic Blues, Order No. AM950697

The Corrs, Order No. AM959849

Elvis Presley, Order No. AM959882

Film Themes, Order No. AM952050

Jazz Classics, Order No. AM952061

Latin, Order No. AM955834

Robbie Williams, Order No. AM972444

60s Hits, Order No. AM955768

70s Hits, Order No. AM968132

80s Hits, Order No. AM955779

90s Hits, Order No. AM944229

...plus many more!